BEI
...I didn't come

They drive through
with dense foliage i
sees...

ALI'S POV: WOMEN + SOM

have brought their
the rain to see the
can say when they
him pass by. Plastic
the children from th
holds up his son. A
window.

INT. INTERCONTINENTAL
DICK SADLER

shouting French to
Folks who look li
Schulberg/Mailer t
half drunk...and ar
out with extortiona
crats like Zairian O
have been cancelled.
no good, passports
There's a stoned H
Bill Cardoso type
Zairian hookers. The
son type is not very
ing Congolese weed.

Produced under licence by
Scholastic Children's Books,
Euston House, 24 Eversholt Street,
London NW1 1DB, UK

Peanuts created by Charles M. Schulz
www.peanuts.com
© 2015 Peanuts Worldwide LLC

Internal designs produced for Scholastic by gas advertising

A division of Scholastic Ltd
London ~ New York ~ Toronto ~ Sydney ~ Auckland
Mexico City ~ New Delhi ~ Hong Kong

First published in the UK by Scholastic Ltd, 2015

ISBN 978 1407 15791 7

Printed in China

2 4 6 8 10 9 7 5 3 1

(to himself,
Jaw broke?
Face busted
to die? Is t
(towards G
'Cause you
man who w
let you win

A tall African (
number "8." As
she has the aud
ALI happens to
at her. She smil
up! THE BELL F

EXT. RING – ALI

goes to the rope
now, comes off
center of the ri
couple of lefts
throws a haym
out of the ring
having avoided t

FOREMAN

gets in a couple
flects. Ali takes
leans way back
seems tired, as
they go diagonal
of the ring, bot
leaning against
BUT...

**EXTREMELY CLOSE:
DEAD SHARP**

He's faking.

FOREMAN

backs Ali into th

ALI

hits Foreman w
launches a short
with a BIG RIGHT

FOREMAN'S

head snaps arou
parabola of light
expectation. Geo
right uppercut,
guiding Forema
Foreman's on th

ALI'S EYES

know the momer

(to himself)
Now...

ALI'S

short, chopping r
head down.

Get ready to go search-crazy with Charlie Brown, Snoopy and the rest of the gang. This book is packed full of things to spot and count, and remember to look out for Woodstock, who appears somewhere on every page.

When you're done, you can check the answers at the back of the book. Have fun searching!

Shadow match

Here are 8 silhouettes of the Peanuts gang. Find the colour pictures that match them and tick the boxes below.

Charlie Brown

Snoopy

Linus Van Pelt

Lucy Van Pelt

Sally Brown

Schroeder

Peppermint Patty

Marcie

One Woodstock is different from the others. Can you find him?

Where's Woodstock?

There are 12 cheeky Woodstocks hidden in this flowery pattern. Can you find them all?

8

The Great Pumpkin

Linus and Charlie Brown are waiting for the Great Pumpkin to rise up on Halloween Night, but some other pals have joined the fun. Who can you see hiding among the pumpkins?

Linus Van Pelt ○   Snoopy ○
Charlie Brown ○   Woodstock ○
Sally Brown ○

Baffling balloons

Snoopy and Woodstock just love balloons.
Spot 12 Woodstocks hidden in the picture.

Then, see if you can find the balloons with special
patterns on them and tick the boxes below.

1 balloon that's like Charlie Brown's shirt
2 basketball balloons
2 lollipop swirl balloons

Spring-time Sally

Sally and Snoopy are having some spring-time fun. Woodstock and his friends want to join in, too. Can you find all 12 of them?

Charlie Brown, Linus and Schroeder are also here. Circle them when you spot them.

15

Let it snow!

Snoopy has been busy building snowmen and he's hidden 6 presents among them. Can you find the gifts and spot the snowman with the missing glove?

Woodstock is feeling festive, too. Can you spot him?

A Charlie Brown Christmas!

Charlie Brown has lost his Christmas candy canes. Help him find all 12 of them in this bright bauble pattern.

Can you spot Woodstock, too?

Sports ace

Charlie Brown and his friends love playing sports. Look carefully at the sporty pictures and find the following things:

- a top hat
- Lucy wearing a spotty top
- an ice cream
- Snoopy wearing sunglasses
- a snowman playing golf
- a blue basketball
- Snoopy playing tennis with a white baseball
- Charlie Brown wearing pink
- Woodstock wearing a crown

21

My Sweet Babboo!

Sally has made 10 Valentine cards for Linus, her 'Sweet Babboo'. See if you can spot them hidden within this heart pattern.

Look out for one very happy Woodstock, too.

World Famous Astronaut

Snoopy has made it! He is the first beagle in space.
Find these space objects floating around him:

5 Snoopy constellations
6 purple planets
3 orange rockets
the odd moon out

How many Woodstocks can you count?

Autumn leaves

Snoopy loves playing in the autumn leaves.
Tick these things when you spot them:

5 oak leaves ● ● ● ● ●

4 maple leaves ● ● ● ●

3 woolly hats ● ● ●

2 leafy twigs ● ●

1 Woodstock ●

Summer fun

School's out – time to head for the beach!
Find these objects in the summery picture:

Woodstock is hiding, too. Can you spot him?

Ace of cards

Find the 10 Charlie Brown cards that match this one.

Don't forget to find Woodstock when you're done.

35

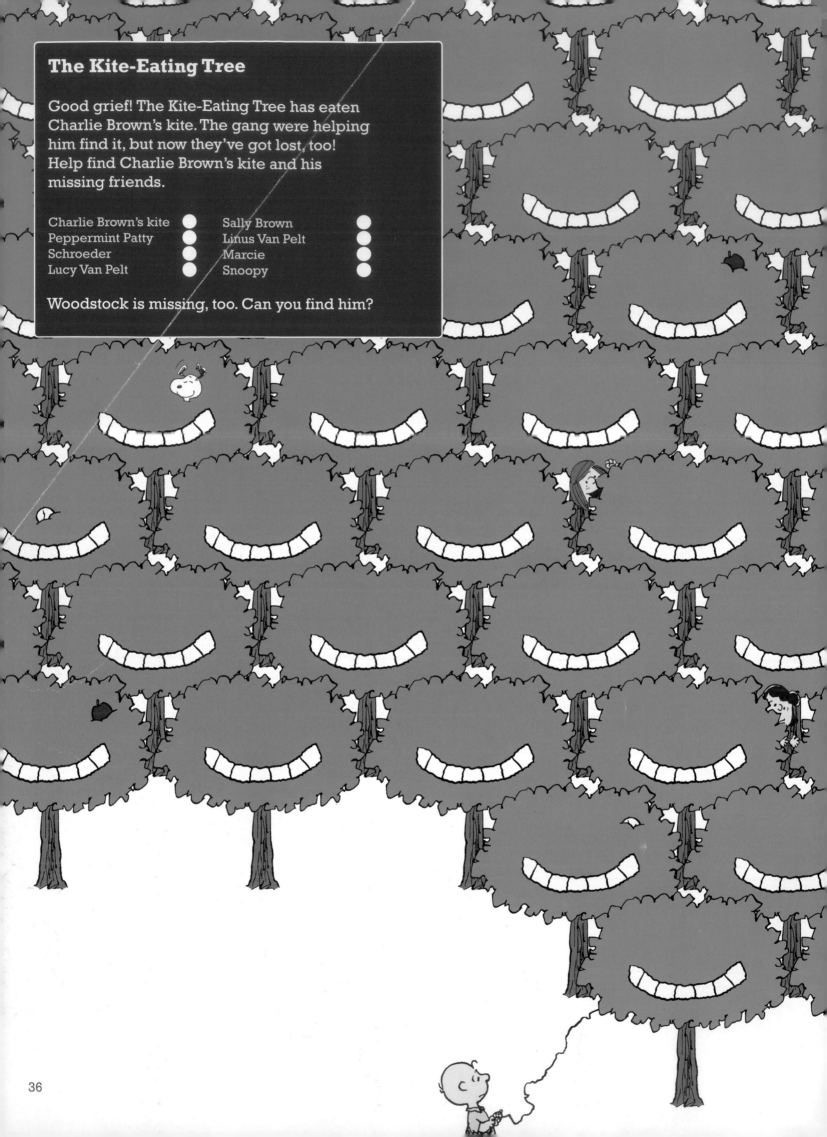

The Kite-Eating Tree

Good grief! The Kite-Eating Tree has eaten Charlie Brown's kite. The gang were helping him find it, but now they've got lost, too! Help find Charlie Brown's kite and his missing friends.

Charlie Brown's kite ⚪   Sally Brown ⚪
Peppermint Patty ⚪   Linus Van Pelt ⚪
Schroeder ⚪   Marcie ⚪
Lucy Van Pelt ⚪   Snoopy ⚪

Woodstock is missing, too. Can you find him?

Party time

It's time to say goodbye to the Peanuts gang.

There's just one last thing to do before you go
– track down Woodstock and 5 of his friends.
Colour them in when you've found them.

Snoopy looks a bit lonely. Why not try drawing
Charlie Brown and the rest of the gang in
the space below?

Shadow match
pages 4 and 5

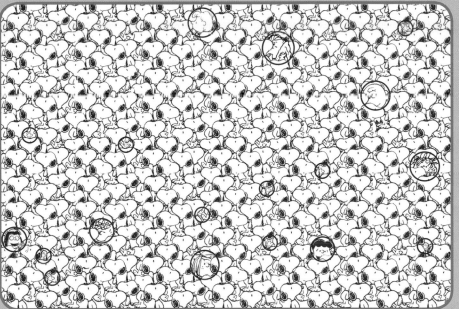

Where's the gang?
pages 6 and 7

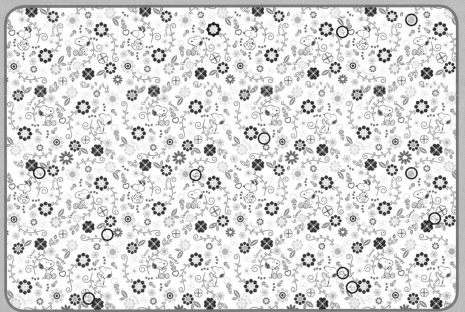

Where's Woodstock?
pages 8 and 9

The Great Pumpkin
pages 10 and 11

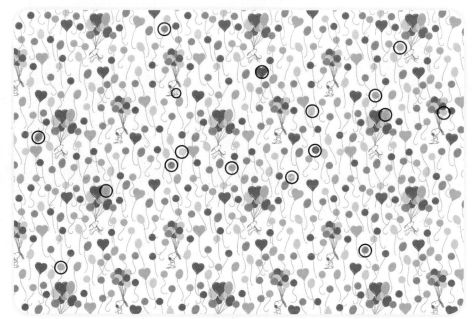

Baffling balloons
pages 12 and 13

Spring-time Sally
pages 14 and 15

Let it snow!
pages 16 and 17

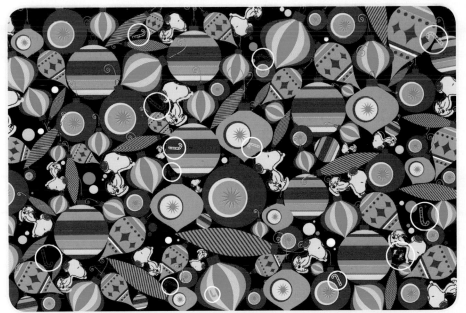

A Charlie Brown Christmas!
pages 18 and 19

Sports ace
pages 20 and 21

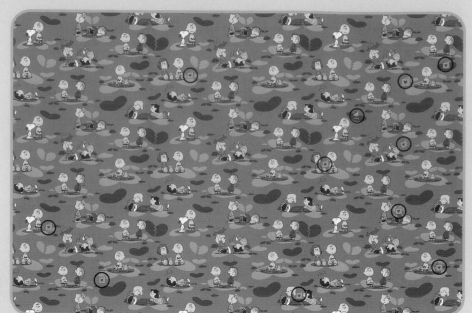

My Sweet Babboo!
pages 22 and 23

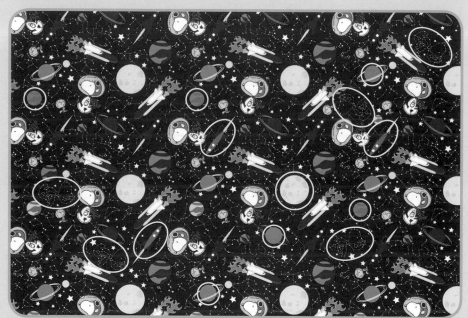

**World Famous
Astronaut**
pages 24 and 25

There are 15 Woodstocks.

A bit of Beethoven
pages 26 and 27

What a mess!
pages 28 and 29

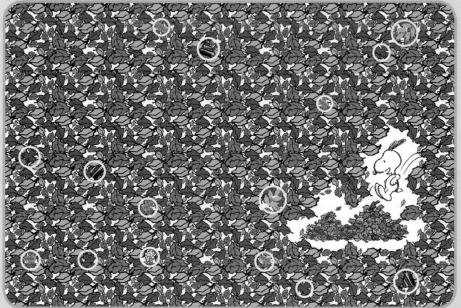

Autumn leaves
pages 30 and 31

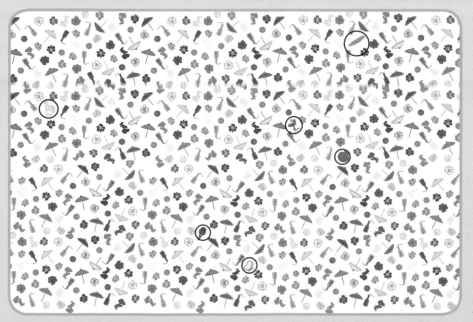

Summer fun
pages 32 and 33

Ace of cards
pages 34 and 35

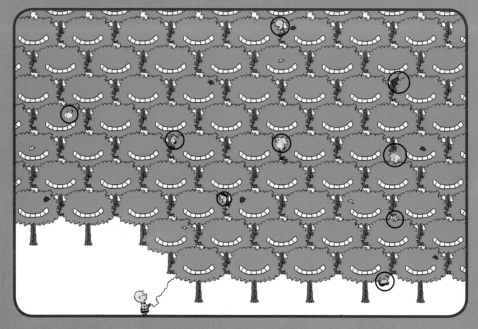

The Kite-Eating Tree
pages 36 and 37

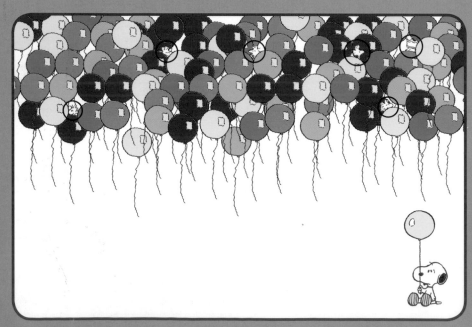

Party time
pages 38 and 39

Also available

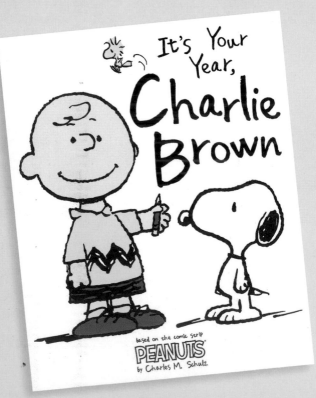